One Monday morning an old man

sat by the window in his flat.

The old man was sad.

He had lost his little cat.

1

Sally looked out of her window.

Her flat was near the old man's flat.

Sally looked at the tree near her flat.

She saw a cat in the tree.

It was a little black cat.

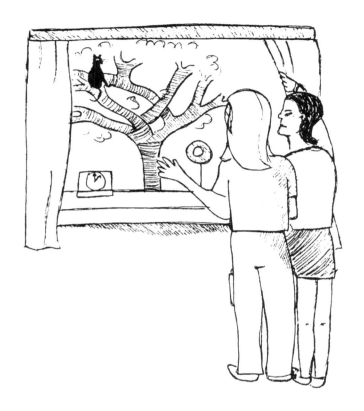

She told Pat.

The little cat sat in the tree.

The little black cat was still up in the tree
that afternoon

It did not come down.

It was still at the top.

Pat went to the tree

and looked up at the cat.

The black cat looked down at Pat.

That afternoon Sally had to got to the shop.

She said to the man at the shop,

"Alittle black cat is in the tree near our flat."

The man in the shop said,

"An old man was here this morning.

He was sad.

He was looking for his little black cat."

Sally said, "Tell the old man,
the cat is in the tree near our flat."

Sally went back to the flat.

Pat was still looking at the tree.

The cat was still up the tree.

Sally said, "An old man is looking

for a little black cat.

He will come and look

at the cat this afternoon."

Pat and Sally looked out of the window.

They saw the old man come to the tree.

The old man looked up at the tree.

The little cat looked down at the old man.

The man did not look sad.

Now he looked happy.

The cat looked down.

The man looked up.

The man said, "Jump little cat.

Jump into my arms."

The cat jumped.

It jumped into the man's arms.

Pat and Sally saw the happy man
and the black cat go home.

The little cat was in the man's arms.